DEAN

MR. MEN   LITTLE MISS
MR. MEN™ LITTLE MISS™ © THOIP (a SANRIO company)

Diddly Doodles Mr. Men © 2018 THOIP (a SANRIO company)
Printed and published under licence from Penguin Random House LLC
First published in Great Britain 2018
by Dean, an imprint of Egmont UK Limited,
The Yellow Building, 1 Nicholas Road, London W11 4AN. All rights reserved

ISBN 978 0 6035 7636 2
70301/002
Printed in Great Britain

Stay safe online. Egmont is not responsible for content hosted by third parties.

Egmont takes its responsibility to the planet and its inhabitants very seriously.
We aim to use papers from well-managed forests run by responsible suppliers.

Mr Small is very small. Probably the smallest person you'll ever see in your whole life. Doodle Mr Small's house under a daisy.

Mr Tall is very, very tall. Quite the tallest person you've ever met. Doodle some more things for him to tower over.

Tickles are small and round, and they have arms that stretch and stretch and stretch. Draw Mr Tickle's extraordinarily long arm tickling Mr Strong or Mr Happy.

Doodle some more Mr Men trying to escape his tickles!

Little Miss Sunshine and her friends
are busy in the garden.

can you doodle some delicate daisies, tall sunflowers and beautiful butterflies?

Not all of the Mr Men are happy. Mr Grumpy is quite the most bad-tempered person you can imagine.

Doodle what is making him so grumpy.

Mr Mean is usually very miserable.
But he's happy today as he's counting
all his money.

Draw even
more money
for him
to count.

Watch out, Little Miss Naughty is about!
Naughty by name and naughty by nature.

Who is she going to leap out at?

Poor Mr Bump just can't help having little accidents. Can you doodle what he has slipped on and bumped into?

don't forget to add some plasters and bandages too.

When things go wrong, Little Miss Hug is always there with a perfectly-fitting hug to make everything better.

Can you doodle
Little Miss Hug giving
Mr Bump, Mr Small and
Little Miss Bossy a hug?
After all, everyone
needs a hug!

Roll up! Roll up! Welcome to the Mr Men circus! Mr Funny is here to make you roar with laughter.

Doodle Mr Funny and his friends doing the funniest things you can imagine.

Mr Bounce and Little Miss Somersault
could be circus acrobats.

What is
Mr Bounce
bouncing
over?

Where is
Little Miss
Somersault
somersaulting
to?

Mr Strong is the strongest person in the whole wide world. Look, he can even lift an elephant above his head!

Can you doodle some other heavy things for him to push, pull and lift?

Mr Skinny doesn't look skinny any more in this mirror!

Create your own big, small, tall and wobbly Mr Men in this hall of mirrors.

How to draw Mr Bump

Step 1

Get started by ...

Drawing an oval-shaped body with small arms and legs.

Step 2

Next ...

His bandages are slightly curved lines - he'll need lots!

step 3

And then ...

Add his eyes and his smile (remember it is half hidden by bandages).

step 4

Finally ...

Colour him in bright blue, leaving just his bandages white.

Draw your own Mr Bump here.

Here comes trouble ... Little Miss Trouble!
Draw what she is painting on the wall.

Little Miss Splendid is shopping for some rather splendid hats, bags and shoes.

Draw some more for her to choose.

Doodle some hair, hats and accessories on these Little Miss!

Little Miss Princess

Little Miss Dotty

Little Miss Naughty

Little Miss Bossy

Little Miss Splendid

Little Miss Chatterbox

Little Miss Giggles

Little Miss Sunshine

It's time for lunch. Mr Greedy likes to eat, but Mr Skinny has hardly any appetite at all. Mr Funny and Little Miss Dotty eat the silliest things!

Mr Silly lives in Nonsenseland where everything is as silly as can be. The trees are pink and the grass is blue.
In Nonsenseland the animals even wear clothes!

Can you draw some animals wearing funny clothes? Then finish the picture with your silliest colours.

In Nonsenseland, they hold a competition for the silliest idea of the year. This house looked perfectly normal until it was wallpapered on the outside!

Can you decorate the house and come up with your own silly idea to make Little Miss Giggles laugh?!

Everything about Mr Topsy-Turvy is either upside down, or inside out or back to front - topsy-turvy in fact.

Mr Fussy and Mr Clumsy are cousins,
but they are really very different.
Just look at them!

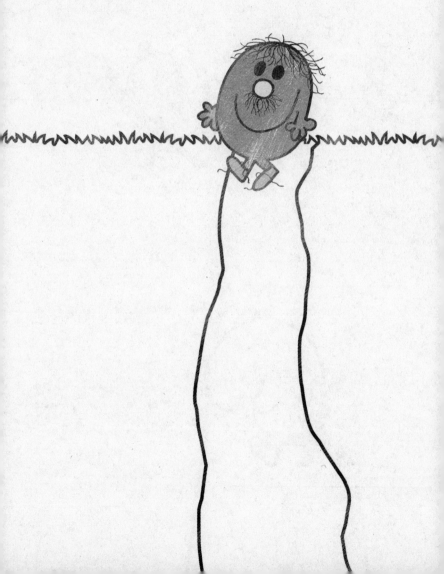

Mr Lazy lives in Sleepyland which is a very lazy-looking and sleepy place.
Mr Slow looks perfectly at home here.

Mr Noisy is a very, very noisy person indeed.

Can you draw Mr Noisy a noisy friend? Maybe it could be a swashbuckling pirate or a T-Rex!

Mr Quiet likes a quiet life.

Mr Jelly is frightened of anything and everything. The slightest little thing will make him turn to jelly.

Doodle some sandcastles!

Little Miss Sunshine and her friends are on holiday at the seaside.

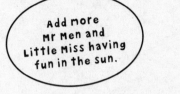

Add more Mr Men and Little Miss having fun in the sun.

Mr Mischief and his friends are up in the air! Doodle some more Mr Men flying through the clouds.

Little Miss Twins live in Twoland where there are two of everything! Can you copy the pictures to make sure they're matching?

Doodle some hair and hats on these Mr Men!

Mr Funny

Mr Cool

Mr Grumpy

Mr Muddle

Mr Clever

Mr Grumble

Mr Fussy

Mr Strong

It looks like it's someone's birthday!
Whose birthday could it be?

Doodle them in and finish drawing their party, including a special present.

Everyone had a great time at the party!
Draw all the friends together in
this photograph.

How to draw Mr Strong

Step 1

Get started by ...

Drawing a square, leaving space for his arms and legs.

Step 2

Next ...

Add his small, strong arms and legs.

step 3

And then ...

He needs his smart little hat, happy eyes and smile.

step 4

Finally ...

Colour him a strong red with a green hat.

DRAW YOUR OWN MR STRONG HERE.

The Mr Men have some splendidly silly and muddled houses. Mr Funny lives in a teapot and Mr Nonsense's house is in a tree!

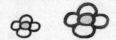

Finish Mr Funny's house and draw a very silly-looking house for Mr Nonsense!

Who lives in this house?
Decorate the rooms and add furniture
to create a home fit for one of the
Mr Men or Little Miss.

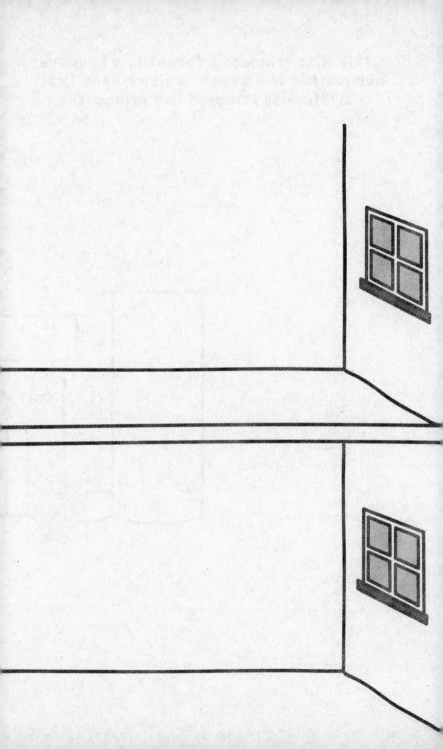

Little Miss Princess's father is a king and her mother is a queen, which means that Little Miss Princess is a princess.

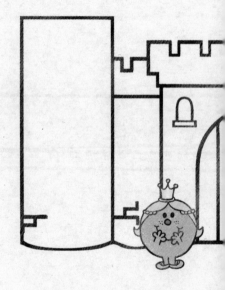

Create a castle fit for a princess. There could be turrets, a drawbridge and a moat.

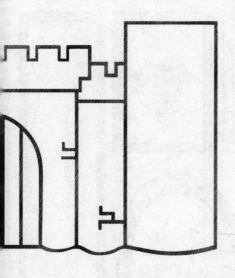

Fill the frames with cute pictures of Little Miss Princess's friends.

Would you like to live in a palace like Little Miss Princess or a teapot house like Mr Funny?

Create your own Mr Men-style house in your favourite Mr Men land.

Colour in the Mr Men and Little Misses before doodling some more.

Use the shapes to get you started.

Mr Happy

Little Miss Trouble

Little Miss Princess

Mr Cheerful

Mr Noisy

Mr Nosey

Little Miss Tiny

Mr Mean

Mr Bump

Little Miss Naughty

Little Miss Curious is very curious.
She would like to know who your favourite
Mr men or Little Miss are.

Little Miss Chatterbox loves to chat. You can't get a word in edgeways or sideways or anyways.

Create a comic strip by doodling in other Mr Men and Little Miss and what they're saying to each other.

Mr Impossible can do the most amazing
things. Finish the pictures to show just
what he can do!

Mr Daydream is dreaming about his next adventure. What could it be?

Howdy partner! The Mr Men are in the Wild West! Yee hah! Finish their cowboy adventure.

Don't forget to add a sheriff to keep order!

5, 4, 3, 2, 1. The Mr Men have blasted into space!

Draw more Mr Men in their spacesuits and some aliens for them to meet!

Mr Strong and his friends are defending Little Miss Princess's castle. Finish the brave knights and draw their attackers!

Ahoy there, me hearties! Shiver me timbers, the Mr Men are having a pirate adventure.

Doodle the rest of the pirate crew and their treasure chest, full of gold.

How to draw
Little Miss Giggles

Step 1

Get started by drawing a round body with little arms and legs.

Step 2

Next ...

Draw her eyes, nose and giggling mouth!

step 3

And then ...

Add some curved lines for her hair and her ribbons.

step 4

Finally ...

Colour her in blue, with red hair and a yellow nose and ribbons. Don't forget to add her freckles!

Draw your own Little Miss Giggles.

Turn the shapes into your favourite Mr Men and Little Miss.

Little Miss Fun

Mr Small

Now it's your turn to create your own Mr Men or Little Miss book cover.

by ....